Sticker
Zoo

Designed by
Carly Davies

Words by Sam Smith

You can make all the zoo animals in this book
using one or more of the stickers at the back.
Then draw on details with a felt-tip pen.

Here's one way you could make a lion.

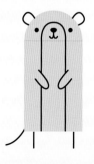

You could show some meerkats peeking out from their burrows.

Combine different
stickers to create
lots of bright birds.

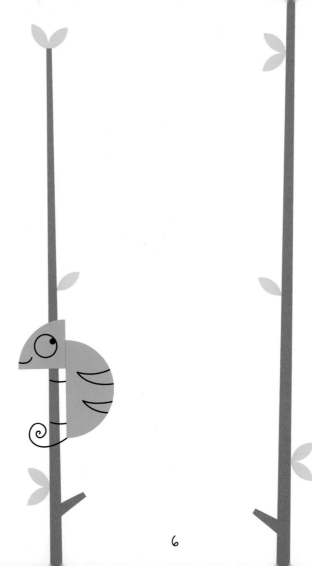

Stick some more chameleons in the trees.

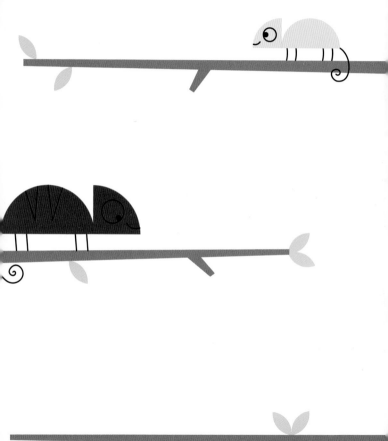

Add some more elephants playing in the water.

Lions have manes...

... but cubs and lionesses don't.

Add more hippos
poking their heads
out of the water.

Draw triangles
to give your
tigers stripes.

Add lots more penguins in
the water and on the ice.

Draw spots on
your giraffes.

19

Some of your monkeys could be swinging on the vines.

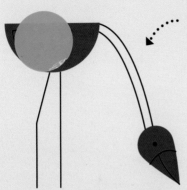

You could show some flamingos dipping their beaks in the water.

Fill the page with
bright-winged
butterflies.

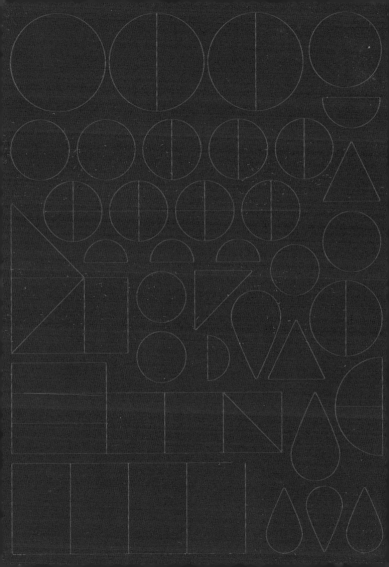